The History of Mammals

W R Hamilton

Trustees of the British Museum (Natural History)
London 1972

Printed in England by
Balding + Mansell Ltd
London and Wisbech
Publication No 714
ISBN 0 565 00714 9

Preface

This book is for the general reader with no previous knowledge of geology or zoology. It describes many of the mammals that have risen to importance, particularly, during the last 70 million years. Most of the illustrations are from drawings, specimens or models in the Fossil Mammal Gallery of the British Museum (Natural History).

Contents

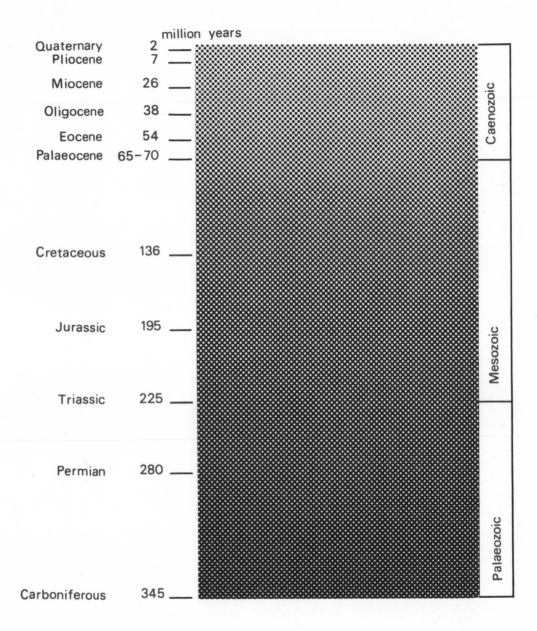

Early mammals

Dogs, cats, mice, elephants, whales, bats, men and most other familiar animals are mammals and share a number of important characteristics. They are warm blooded and have a hairy body-covering, they give birth to live young which are suckled on milk produced by the mother during a period of parental care which may be extended beyond weaning, they have highly developed brains and sense organs, they walk with the limbs held under the body, have complex teeth and chew with a precise action. Some of these features are found in other groups ; for example, the birds are warm-blooded, have highly developed sense organs and walk with the limbs held under the body, but they do not give birth to live young, do not suckle their young and have feathers instead of hair.

Mammals evolved from the mammal-like reptiles or Synapsida during the Triassic Period over 200 million years ago. The Synapsida was one of the earliest groups of reptiles to appear and members of the group were the dominant large land animals throughout the Permian Period before the development of the dinosaurs.

Thrinaxodon

2

A pantothere

Some of the synapsids developed features more usually associated with mammals and the early Triassic *Thrinaxodon* was similar to the ancestor of the mammals. The development of other mammalian characters is related to the high level of activity characteristic of members of the group and this is probably the key to the success of the mammals.

Some of the earliest known fossil mammals are from rocks of Triassic age in Lesotho and slightly younger rocks in South Wales, both being about 200 million years old. The Lesotho mammals include *Megazostrodon* which is known from an almost complete and beautifully preserved skeleton, which is by far the oldest yet found. Deposits in South Wales have yielded thousands of teeth and bones of the small mammals *Eozostrodon* (*Morganucodon*) and *Kuehneotherium* which are closely related to *Megazostrodon* and all are placed in the pantothere group of early mammals.

A multituberculate

The skull of a multituberculate

An echidna

Early mammals were small and shrew-like and probably fed upon insects and other small invertebrates, fruit and eggs. The dinosaurs were the dominant large and medium-sized land animals until the end of the Cretaceous, about 70 million years ago, while the mammals remained small and were a relatively unimportant element of the terrestrial fauna. Most early mammals were omnivorous and were probably nocturnal, competing for food with lizards. During the Jurassic a group of specialized, plant-eating mammals — the multituberculates — arose, which were primitive in body form though possessing large rodent-like front teeth for gathering food, and wide grinding cheek teeth. Multituberculates were probably rodent-like in habits and general appearance. They became extinct about 45 million years ago after a history of over 100 million years, which is far longer than any other mammalian order.

At the end of Cretaceous times about 70 million years ago, the dinosaurs had become extinct and the way was open for the mammals to radiate and expand into a position of dominance on land.

The two main divisions of modern mammals — marsupials and placentals — arose from a common ancestor in Jurassic times, about 150 million years ago: long before this the monotremes (platypus and echidna) had separated from the ancestral mammalian stock. These three surviving groups are clearly defined by features of their reproduction. Monotremes lay eggs and are reptile-like in many other features; they represent a condition reached by the ancestors of the mammals in late Triassic or early Jurassic times. The young of marsupials are born alive, but are poorly developed and must continue their development in a pouch or 'marsupium' from which the name 'marsupial' is derived. The marsupials represent a condition which was reached by mammals in early Cretaceous times. The young of advanced mammals are well developed at birth as they are retained in the mother's body for a long period, obtaining nutrition through a special membrane which is called a 'placenta' from which the term 'placental mammal' is derived.

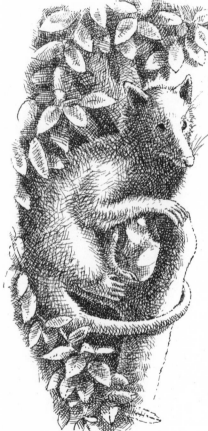

Opossum

The marsupials were originally a North American group and they were relatively successful in North America in middle Cretaceous times. Early marsupials were probably similar in appearance and habits to the living opossum (*Didelphis*).

Placental mammals originated at the same time as marsupials; they were originally successful in Eurasia and in late Cretaceous times they also became an important North American group. Ancestral placental mammals belong to a group known as the Palaeoryctidae, and were shrew-like in appearance and omnivorous. The group gave rise directly to the Carnivora (dogs, cats, weasels, mongooses) and to the ancestral stock (Condylarthra) from which the elephants, pigs and cattle, and horses developed. The nearest living relatives of the palaeoryctids are the tenrecs and golden moles. A second important group – the Leptictidae – was closely related to the Palaeoryctidae and gave rise to the bats, rodents, primates and rabbits as well as the living members of the Insectivora (hedgehogs, moles and shrews).

At the beginning of the Tertiary, about 70 million years ago, several of the main mammalian groups were already in existence including the Carnivora, Insectivora, Primates, Rodentia, Lagomorpha (rabbits) and Chiroptera (bats), but it was only during the Tertiary that the mammals became a really important group evolving into many diverse and highly specialized forms and increasing in body size to exploit the terrestrial environment. The history of mammals in the Tertiary is one of increasing specialization to perform efficiently within a very narrow range of activities. Thus with increasing competition for food and resources, many forms have become highly specialized to restricted and particular environments and diets. In contrast other groups have remained unspecialized and have retained the ancestral omnivorous diet.

Mammalian features

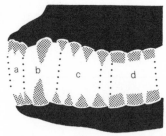

a   incisors
b   canine
c   premolars
d   molars

The type of food of a mammal is usually reflected in features of the teeth, which are the hardest parts of the body and are therefore most often fossilized. Consequently much of our knowledge of fossil mammals is derived from interpretation of their teeth. Mammalian teeth are differentiated into regions having different functions. The front teeth or incisors are used for nipping and biting, and are usually small and simple. Behind them is a large, strong tooth – the canine – which is used for stabbing and is usually a simple spike. The cheek teeth consists of premolars and molars; premolars are used for gripping food and for chewing, while the molars are used for chewing. The crowns of the cheek teeth are usually complex and carry small swellings or cusps which make them more effective for gripping or chewing. Within major groups of mammals the patterns of the cusps are usually similar for all members of the group, and these patterns may be used to identify them and also to assess their relationships to other mammals.

The different types of foods make different demands upon the animal and are reflected in the teeth, skull structure and body form. The earliest mammals were omnivorous, feeding upon flesh, invertebrates and plant material; surviving omnivores include the opossum, rat, pig, and man. Omnivores usually have low-crowned teeth with rounded cusps which are suitable for dealing with all kinds of food.

Insectivores, as their name implies, feed upon insects. It is difficult to obtain sufficient insects to sustain a large animal, and insectivorous mammals are usually small, e.g. shrews, tenrecs and many bats; however some of the anteaters are able to attain relatively large size as they utilize a specialized and concentrated food source. The cheek teeth of insectivores have very high, sharp cusps for piercing the hard outer coat of their food. Anteaters have evolved strong front limbs for opening the ants' nests and long snouts and tongues for collecting sufficient insects quickly; however, since the ants are not chewed the cheek teeth have degenerated into small pegs or have been lost entirely.

Flesh-eating mammals – carnivores – may be specialized for

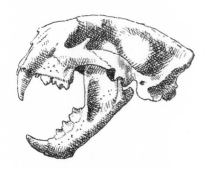

The skull of a cat

The skull of a horse

several types of food, including invertebrates, other vertebrates or carrion. Animals which feed upon large vertebrates generally attain a medium mammalian size. All carnivorous land mammals are good runners chasing their prey with an efficient bounding gait. The limbs are not greatly lengthened and the body remains supple; claws, separate toes, large canines and short strong jaws are required for the efficient holding and killing of prey. The cheek teeth are usually specialized for slicing the food into pieces small enough to swallow, but the crushing facets of the teeth may be entirely lost as meat is easily digested and does not require chewing. Some living carnivorous mammals are cats, dogs, weasels and hyaenas; all are members of the order Carnivora.

Plant-eating mammals or herbivores utilize different food sources, including leaves and twigs 'browsers' and grasses 'grazers'. Plant foods require different specialized structures and organs in the mammals since they are less nutritious than flesh and more must be eaten; they are also more difficult to digest, demanding a larger and more complex digestive system than that of a carnivore.

Herbivores can attain large body size; a galloping gait is usually adopted by large herbivorous mammals, though the flexing of the back apparent in the bounding gait of carnivores still plays a part. The limbs increase in length in fast-running forms and the toes become reduced in number and develop hooves instead of claws. Specializations for fast running do not usually develop in very large land mammals such as elephants, as the limbs of these animals are adapted for supporting the large weight of the animal.

Plant foods cause considerable wear on the teeth as they often contain abrasive constituents and usually require much chewing; thus the teeth of herbivores tend to develop high crowns with complex patterns. The crowns are highest in grazing animals since grasses are the most abrasive. The face is usually long to accommodate the battery of cheek teeth which tends to become larger as the premolars adopt a chewing function. The crowns of the cheek teeth have a flattened chewing surface for crushing the food and the slicing action is usually lost.

As plant material is a primary food source, a balanced fauna always contains more herbivores than carnivores; thus in collections of fossil mammals the herbivores nearly always predominate. Living herbivores include cows, horses, rhinoceroses, elephants, rodents and rabbits.

Flesh-eating mammals

The two main groups of flesh-eating mammals in existence during the Tertiary are called the Creodonta and Carnivora, both originating from the palaeoryctids during late Cretaceous times. The creodonts were the dominant flesh-eating mammals from Palaeocene to Oligocene times, after which the members of the Carnivora increased in importance; they had virtually replaced all the creodonts by Miocene times. The creodonts became extinct in Pliocene times, and members of the Carnivora have survived as the cats, dogs, bears, raccoons, weasels, mongooses, hyaenas, seals, sealions and walruses of today.

Features of the teeth and wrist are used to distinguish creodonts from members of the Carnivora. In both groups the cheek teeth are blade-like and act as scissors in chewing the food. In members of the Creodonta the main slicing teeth are usually the molars and more than one upper and lower molar is usually specialized for shearing, though less so than in the Carnivora. The shearing teeth in the Carnivora are always the last upper premolar and the first lower molar. These may become highly specialized; thus in cats the first upper molar is very small and the other upper molars are lost, but the upper shearing tooth is extremely long and blade-like. In the wrists of all advanced members of the Carnivora three small bones have become fused to form a larger single element, which never occurs in members of the Creodonta.

The creodonts were primitive in structure, their brains were relatively small and they were presumably of low intelligence. The creodont skull is very low, and a strong ridge is developed at the back for the attachment of the jaw muscles as the cranium is too small to provide a sufficient area of attachment. Creodonts were less specialized for running than members of the Carnivora and the number of toes is rarely reduced, whereas in the dogs and cats there are only four functional toes and a 'dew claw' representing the reduced first toe. The small brain of the creodonts may have been an important factor in their decline, as during Eocene and early Oligocene times advanced herbivores such as the artiodactyls and perissodactyls (see Chapter 4) were developing, and

Oxyaena

Hyaenodon

the slower moving, less intelligent early herbivores were declining. The more advanced types of prey required more sophisticated hunting techniques of the predator and the development of these by the larger brained members of the Carnivora caused them to be more successful than the creodonts.

One group of the Creodonta — the Oxyaenidae — included forms which were comparable in habits and appearance to the living weasels, badgers, civets and mongooses. They were long-bodied, short-limbed forms with relatively wide skulls carrying strong jaw muscles. The early Eocene form *Oxyaena* was about the size of a wolverine and probably had a similar way of life — it may have given rise to the middle Eocene *Patriofelis*, which was the size of a bear.

Members of the other creodont group — the Hyaenodontidae — were very successful in early Tertiary times. They were probably similar in habits to the cats, dogs and hyaenas and some became very large. One form — *Machaeroides* — developed long upper canines and was presumably similar in habits to the sabre-toothed cats. The most successful creodont was *Hyaenodon* which was represented by many species and is known from Oligocene deposits in Europe, Asia, Africa and North America, and in Britain on the Isle of Wight. In the Oligocene deposits of the White River, Dakota and Nebraska, U.S.A., *Hyaenodon* is represented by six species, whose sizes range from that of a small dog to that of a lion.

The largest creodont known is from Miocene deposits in Africa and the Indian region. It was about the size of a grizzly bear, weighed about 800 kg and had a skull about 60 cm in length. The skull is very wide and the front teeth are short and stout, which suggests that the animal could crush bones and was probably similar in habits to the hyaena. The creodonts declined during Oligocene and Miocene times and *Dissopsalis* from the late Miocene and Pliocene of India is the last known member of the order.

The order Carnivora includes all the familiar larger flesh-eating animals living today. The ancestral stock of the order is the Miacidae

Miacis

which was contemporary with the Creodonta throughout the Palaeocene and Eocene. Miacids had larger brains than creodonts, and their shearing teeth were the last upper premolar and the first lower molar as in all later members of the Carnivora. *Miacis* was a small, tree-living form which probably inhabited forest and woodland, feeding upon small vertebrates, invertebrates, eggs and fruit. Remains of *Miacis* are relatively rare, but a complete skull of the closely related *Viverravus* is known from the Upper Eocene deposits of southern Hampshire.

Advanced members of the Carnivora are divided into two major groups: the dogs and their relatives (Arctoidea) and the cats and their relatives (Aeluroidea). These two stocks became divided in late Eocene times and during the Oligocene radiation in both groups gave rise to diverse forms variously specialized for different prey and ways of life.

The Aeluroidea includes the cats (Felidae), genets and civets (Viverridae) and hyaenas (Hyaenidae). Viverrids are small, tree-living, forest-dwelling forms which are little different from the miacids. They survive in the Old World tropics, and fossil remains of *Viverra* are known from the Miocene of Europe and India. Hyaenas are advanced flesh-eating animals with specialized dentitions enabling them to crush bones to obtain the marrow, thus utilizing the prey more fully and increasing their effectiveness as scavengers. Features of the skull related to bone crushing are a short face, a very high crest for the attachment of the huge jaw muscles which are accommodated in the very wide arches behind the eyes, and very strong teeth. Hyaenas are common in deposits of Pliocene age, especially from Pikermi and Samos in Greece, and from India.

Before the Pleistocene most cats were of the sabre-toothed variety, having small lower canines and huge, curving upper canines. *Hoplophoneus* from the Oligocene of North America, one of the earliest cats, had well-developed sabre-teeth. The back of the skull is high in the sabre-toothed cats to accommodate the great neck muscles and the longer jaw muscles, necessary for the

Hoplophoneus

use of the canines. Aspects of these teeth and associated structures of the skull became exaggerated through the later Tertiary. One of the most advanced sabre-toothed cats was *Smilodon* from the Pleistocene of North America.

Modern cats kill by leaping on to the back of the prey and biting into the base of the neck or where the skull joins the neck, thus severing the spinal cord or breaking the neck. This killing method requires short equal-sized upper and lower canines, and is effective for small or medium-sized, relatively long-necked, fast-running prey such as antelopes, cattle or horses; but it would not be effective for large, thick-skinned, short-necked, heavily muscled prey such as the entelodonts, brontotheres, gomphotheres, deinotheres and rhinoceroses which were common in middle and late Tertiary times. This type of prey requires specialized killing techniques for which the sabre-toothed cats were adapted. Their killing method was to use the upper canines for inflicting large open wounds by stabbing and slashing, causing the prey to bleed copiously. This method is slow but this is not important with large, slow-moving prey. With the decline of the large, thick-skinned animals during the Pliocene and Pleistocene, the sabre-toothed cats also declined, and modern cats such as lions, leopards and cheetahs replaced them.

The modern type of cat is first known from the middle Tertiary. The group increased in importance as the new groups of medium-sized, fast-running herbivores such as the horses, deer, giraffes, antelopes and cattle evolved. *Pseudaelurus* is a typical modern type of cat, and is first known from the early Miocene of Africa and Europe.

The Arctoidea comprises the dogs (Canidae); weasels, otters and badgers (Mustelidae); raccoons (Procyonidae); and bears (Ursidae). One group of dogs – the Amphicyoninae – became relatively large and bear-like, and *Amphicyon*, which is known from the middle Tertiary of Eurasia and North America, was about the same size as a brown bear and was probably similar in habits. The bears probably arose from the dogs, and some forms, such as

Smilodon

A dire wolf

the Pleistocene cave bear, attained great size. The dire wolf from the Pleistocene of Rancho la Brea, California, developed a heavy skull and teeth and may have been similar to the hyaena in habit. Seals, sealions and walruses probably arose from the Arctoidea during Oligocene or early Miocene times. They represent an advance in aquatic adaptations over the otters which were already specialized fishers in Oligocene times, when forms such as the small otter *Potamotherium* flourished in the lakes of Europe.

The history of the Carnivora is one of specialization to more efficient predation on different types of prey in different environments. The sabre-toothed cats which hunted slow-moving, thick-skinned prey developed a very specialized killing technique and declined when their prey became scarce. The cats are primarily forest and woodland hunters, using ambush and stalking in preference to running down their prey, which they kill by breaking the neck. The short face; strong canines; sharp, retractable claws; and solitary habit are related to these hunting methods. Exceptions to this are the cheetah and the lion. The cheetah is a specialized running animal and significantly the claws are blunt and non-retractable as in the dogs. Though retaining the characteristic cat-hunting pattern of ambush and stalking, the lion has modified this for a plains environment by adopting a pack ('pride') hunting method. The cats expanded as the prey for which they were specialized proliferated, and they are now at the peak of their development.

In contrast the dogs are primarily plains-dwelling forms. They run down their prey, which they weaken by slashing wounds inflicted on the flanks and legs. The long face, good running ability, blunt claws and pack-living habit are related to this hunting technique.

Plant-eating mammals

Phenacodus

There are three main groups of large, plant-eating mammals: the elephants; horses and rhinoceroses; and cattle, antelopes, deer, pigs and hippopotamuses. These groups originated from an order of generalized, primitive herbivores – the Condylarthra – which was dominant in Palaeocene and early Eocene times. Most of the condylarths were small; *Phenacodus*, which was the size of a sheep, was one of the largest members of the group. *Phenacodus* is well known from fossil remains of late Palaeocene and early Eocene age: it had five-toed feet with small hooves, a heavily built body, a long tail and low-crowned cheek teeth with rounded cusps indicating that it fed upon soft vegetation. The group to which *Phenacodus* belongs – the Phenacodontidae – gave rise to the horses and probably also the elephants and a major group of South American herbivores, the Litopterna.

Another group of condylarths – the Meniscotheriidae – includes small rabbit-like animals such as *Meniscotherium*, with high-crowned cheek teeth bearing crescentic cusps which indicate that it was specialized for a herbivorous habit. However, its foot structure is primitive and it had five toes and claws. Members of another condylarth group – the Mesonychidae – were common in Eocene

Meniscotherium

A tillodont

A taeniodont

Uintatherium

times: they were wolf-like in appearance but were probably omnivorous. Some mesonychids attained great size: *Andrew-sarchus* from the Eocene of Mongolia is the largest known condylarth, having a skull almost a metre in length, the animal probably being larger than a grizzly bear. The mesonychid condylarths probably gave rise to the whales (Cetacea).

During the early Tertiary several short-lived groups of mammals arose to exploit the large herbivore niche, including the tillodonts which stemmed from the condylarths and had large incisors similar to those of rodents. The taeniodonts probably arose at the end of the Cretaceous and were fairly successful until the end of the Eocene; they had very powerful front limbs, probably an adaptation for digging. The largest mammals of the early Tertiary were the members of the orders Pantodonta and Dinocerata. The Pantodonta includes *Coryphodon*, a large herbivore which was common in North America in early Tertiary times and is known from Europe, including the London area. The Dinocerata was a very successful order and is well represented from Eocene deposits in Mongolia and North America. *Uintatherium* from the Green River deposits of North America is the best known member of the order, standing about $1\frac{1}{2}$ metres high at the shoulder and having a body length of about 3 metres. These early herbivore groups declined towards the end of the Eocene as the more slowly developing modern herbivore groups became increasingly important.

Horses and rhinoceroses The group which includes the horses, tapirs and rhinoceroses is called the Perissodactyla. In all members of this order the axis of the foot passes through the middle toe and reduction in the number of toes tends to leave an odd number of functional toes on each foot; thus the horse has one toe and the rhinoceros three on each foot. The ancestor of this order is *Hyracotherium* (also known as *Eohippus* or the 'dawn horse'). This small, hare-like animal is known from deposits of late Palaeocene and Eocene age in North America and from the Eocene of Europe. *Hyracotherium* had slender limbs and low-crowned cheek teeth, it was a browser and probably lived in

Andrewsarchus

Pliohippus

Hyracotherium

forests and swamps, and it had four toes on its front feet and three toes on the hind feet.

The evolutionary history of the horses is very well known from fossils. It mostly occurred in North America with occasional invasions of Eurasia throughout the later Tertiary. *Mesohippus* developed from the smaller *Hyracotherium* and is known from deposits of Oligocene age. It had three toes on each foot, its teeth were low-crowned and it was probably a swamp and forest dweller, similar in habit to some of the small deer. By Miocene times the horses had migrated to the plains and were becoming specialized grazers. The Miocene horse *Merychippus* had high-crowned, complex cheek teeth, but still retained three toes on each foot, though the middle toe was dominant indicating an increasing adaptation towards fast running. *Merychippus* was about the size

Mesohippus

Merychippus

Hyracodon

of a donkey and its face was longer than that of *Mesohippus* to accommodate the larger teeth. The modern horse probably evolved from *Pliohippus* which was the first one-toed horse and was fully adapted to a plains environment and possessed high cheek teeth, a long face and a large brain.

The history of the horses is a story of increasing specialization to plains-dwelling and grazing. The changes occurring between *Hyracotherium* and the modern horse reflect the different demands made upon the animals in their adaptation to the different environments. The increase in height and complexity of the cheek teeth and the lengthening of the face are related to the animals' increase in size and their diet of abrasive grasses; while the increased intelligence and running ability are specializations to plains dwelling.

Tapirs and rhinoceroses originated in Eocene times and were an important group for the rest of the Tertiary. In Oligocene times a group of long-limbed rhinoceroses — the Hyracodontidae — developed, which were probably plains-dwelling animals and evolved features later developed in horses. They had long limbs and feet with the centre toe dominant, and high-crowned cheek teeth. *Hyracodon* from the Middle Oligocene of North America is a typical member of the group and like the later horses was probably a plains-dwelling grazer. Another group of rhinoceroses attained gigantic size; *Paraceratherium* (also known as *Indricotherium* or *Baluchitherium*) from the Oligocene of Asia was the largest land mammal that has ever lived, standing over 5 metres (17 feet) at the shoulder, having a body length of over 8 metres and probably weighing about 16 tons. This animal was a browser, and like the giraffe probably fed upon high vegetation in forests and woodland.

Two other important fossil groups — the brontotheres and chalicotheres — are related to the horses. Brontotheres (also known as titanotheres) were abundant in Eocene times in North America and in late Eocene and Oligocene times in Asia. One of the most advanced members of the group was *Brontotherium* from the Oligocene of North America, which was the size of a modern

Paraceratherium

Moropus

Brontotherium

elephant and had a huge, double horn on its nose. The chalicotheres were the strangest perissodactyls; they had very strong
front legs which were longer than the hind limbs and the feet
carried great claws, which they probably used for digging up the
roots on which they fed (they are the only clawed perissodactyls).
Chalicotheres were widespread in middle and later Tertiary times;
Moropus from the Miocene of North America was one of the
largest members of this group.

Moeritherium

Palaeomastodon

Gomphotherium

Elephants, seacows and hyraxes The largest living land mammals – the elephants – are the only survivors of a group which was very important from Oligocene times until only a few thousand years ago. Elephants and their fossil relatives form the order Proboscidea, the name being derived from the trunk or proboscis which is characteristic of most members of the order. Proboscideans appear to be related to the seacows and the hyraxes, as well as to a bizarre fossil group, the Embrithopoda. These groups originated from the condylarths, probably in late Palaeocene or early Eocene times, but their first fossil remains are from deposits of late Eocene and early Oligocene age in North Africa, particularly at the Fayum, Egypt.

The Fayum fauna indicates that the African mammals had been evolving in isolation during the Eocene and suggests that the seacows, hyraxes and elephants originated in Africa. Included in the Fayum fauna are *Moeritherium* and *Palaeomastodon* which are related to the elephants. *Moeritherium* was short-limbed and no larger than a pig, having low-crowned cheek teeth but tusk-like front teeth. It displays features which suggest relationships with elephants and seacows, but it could not have been ancestral to either group since members of both groups are present in the same fauna. However, the ancestral elephant was probably very similar in appearance to *Moeritherium*, being semi-aquatic and feeding upon near-shore vegetation. *Palaeomastodon*, which was much larger than *Moeritherium*, is clearly a member of the Proboscidea and may well have been ancestral to the gomphotheres and elephants. It had single pairs of upper and lower tusks and cheek teeth which are very similar to those of the later gomphotheres.

The commonest member of the Gomphotheriidae was *Gomphotherium*, which is also sometimes called *Trilophodon*, *Tetrabelodon* or *Mastodon*. *Gomphotherium* was almost the same size as a modern elephant, and it had a trunk and large upper and lower tusks; its low-crowned cheek teeth with rounded cusps suggest that it was a browser.

Deinotherium

The deinotheres form a group which is distinct from the other proboscideans, and probably also includes *Barytherium* from the early Oligocene of North Africa. *Deinotherium* had very simple cheek teeth consisting of two or three cross-crests which are suitable for cutting soft plant material or twigs into short lengths for swallowing. *Deinotherium* had a short trunk and lacked upper tusks. Its strangest feature was the presence of a pair of large, curved lower tusks which were probably used for digging or for pulling down the branches of trees. The deinotheres were very successful in Eurasia and Africa from early Miocene to early Pleistocene times and some varieties of *Deinotherium giganteium* became very large, even approaching *Paraceratherium* in body size.

Another group in the Fayum fauna which is probably related to the elephants and hyraxes is the Embrithopoda which is an order with only a single member – *Arsinoitherium*. This animal was larger than a rhinoceros and had two huge horns on its nose. It is known from Lower Oligocene deposits in North Africa and was herbivorous, probably having a way of life similar to the rhinoceros.

Modern hyraxes are small rabbit-like animals which are restricted to Africa and the Middle East. They are well represented in the Fayum fauna and were important medium-sized herbivores in Africa during Oligocene times, with forms such as *Titanohyrax* approaching the size of a rhinoceros. The hyraxes were still an important medium-sized herbivore group in the early Miocene of Africa, including forms such as *Megalohyrax* which were horse-like in habit and appearance. Pliocene hyraxes are known from Africa, Europe and China and the European form *Pliohyrax* was as large as a pony. However, the Pliocene saw the end of the hyraxes as important medium-sized herbivores, and the modern forms comprise a minor part of the African fauna.

Seacows are also related to the elephants, hyraxes and *Arsinoitherium*. They probably originated in early or middle Eocene times in Africa and by virtue of their aquatic adaptations they were able to spread rapidly all over the world. The Pliocene seacow *Felsinotherium* was similar to the modern dugong and is known from

Arsinoitherium

Megalohyrax

numerous remains in central Europe and a few specimens from Britain.

Pigs, hippopotamuses, camels, deer, antelopes and cattle
Members of the order Artiodactyla have been the dominant medium-sized herbivores since middle Oligocene times and are today at the peak of their development, with pigs, hippopotamuses, camels, deer, giraffes, antelopes, cattle, sheep and goats all being important elements in their respective environments. The artiodactyls originated in late Palaeocene times from an unknown condylarth stock; two important features of their limbs distinguish them from other herbivores. First, the axis of the foot passes between the two middle toes, and any reduction which may occur in the number of toes tends to leave an even number on each foot. Thus, pigs have four toes, deer and cattle have two large centre

Archaeotherium

Bothriodon

Cainotherium

toes and two small side-toes, and giraffes have two toes on each foot. Secondly, one of the ankle bones – the astragalus – is also highly characteristic in the artiodactyls, having rotation surfaces at both ends in contrast to other mammals in which only the upper surface allows rotation. This is a specialization for fast running, which allows free rotation in a backwards and forwards direction but restricts sideways movement.

In Oligocene times a group of giant pig-like animals – the Entelodontidae – flourished in North America and Eurasia. These animals had huge skulls, some up to a metre in length with great swellings of bone on the lower jaws and below the eyes. The front teeth were developed to form large tusks which were probably used to dig for roots. *Archaeotherium* from the Oligocene of North America was a member of this successful, but short-lived group.

The hippopotamuses probably originated in Miocene times and since Pliocene times they have flourished. A Pleistocene hippopotamus from East Africa – *Hippopotamus gorgops* – shows more advanced specializations to life in water than the modern hippopotamus (*Hippopotamus amphibius*), in that its eyes were situated in large swellings high on the skull enabling it to raise its eyes only above the water surface. Hippopotamuses originated from a large fossil group, the Anthracotheriidae, which was very successful in middle Tertiary times and survived into the Pleistocene. Anthracotheres were probably pig-like in appearance, but were probably amphibious in habit. Remains of anthracotheres are common in middle Tertiary deposits and numerous specimens of *Bothriodon* have been discovered on the Isle of Wight in deposits of Oligocene age.

The camels and numerous closely related fossil groups were important in middle Tertiary times, and the camels continued to be an important group in North America until well into the Pleistocene. The small, hare-like artiodactyl *Cainotherium* is thought to be related to the camels, though it stood about 30 cm at the shoulder and had a hopping gait similar to that of a hare which it probably also resembled in way of life and appearance. Numerous beauti-

Agriochoerus

Poebrotherium

Tragulus

fully preserved remains of *Cainotherium* have been discovered in Oligocene deposits in the department of Allier, France, and caino-theres were restricted to Europe throughout their history.

The Merycoidodontidae was a very important North American group of medium-sized herbivores during Oligocene and Miocene times. The remains of thousands of individuals of *Merycoidodon* have been discovered in the White River deposits of Dakota and Nebraska, U.S.A., and this animal seems to have been the most important plains-dwelling herbivore. More advanced members of the Merycoidodontidae developed higher-crowned cheek teeth with crescentic cusps, indicating that they fed upon harder plant material and may have been grazers. However, *Promerycochoerus* became quite large and was probably semi-aquatic, while *Agrio-choerus*, which was closely related to the merycoidodonts, developed claws (it is the only clawed artiodactyl) and may have been a tree-dwelling form.

The camels were important in North America in Oligocene and Miocene times. They included gazelle-like forms such as *Poe-brotherium* and *Stenomylus*, and giraffe-like forms such as *Oxydactylus*. The Pleistocene form *Camelops* was closely related to the living camel, though it had not developed a hump, and was probably similar in appearance to the living llamas of South America to which it was also closely related.

Giraffes, deer and bovids (cattle, sheep, goats, antelopes) origi-nated from a group of small deer-like animals – the Tragulidae – which has two living members: the chevrotain (*Tragulus*) of Asia and the water chevrotain (*Hyemoschus*) of Africa. Both are small, forest-dwelling animals, without horns but having large upper tusks which they use for fighting and defence. Tragulids were very common in Oligocene times in Europe and in Miocene times in Africa. The genus *Dorcatherium* from the Miocene of Africa, Asia and Europe is very closely related to the living *Hyemoschus* and was a common and important member of the fauna. During late Oligocene and early Miocene times the giraffoids, of which there are two main groups, became important in Africa. The first group

Giraffokeryx

Prolibytherium

includes the living giraffes and several fossil forms, all of which are relatively long-necked and long-limbed animals. *Giraffokeryx* from the Miocene of India is an interesting form in that its body was similar to the living okapi, to which it is closely related; but it possessed two pairs of horns, one pair being above the eyes and the other on the back of the head. The second group of giraffoids is the sivatheres, which included short-limbed, short-necked forms. *Prolibytherium* from the early Miocene of North Africa is the earliest sivathere known, and was about the size of a sheep with huge, plate-like horns which completely covered the top of its skull. A later member of this group was *Sivatherium* from the Pleistocene of India, which was very large, standing about $2\frac{1}{2}$ metres at the shoulder and having great branching horns. It was probably a forest-dwelling form and had relatively high-crowned teeth, suggesting that it included a high proportion of grass in its diet.

The deer also originated from the tragulids, probably in late Oligocene times. Deer are primarily browsing, forest-dwelling forms inhabiting the northern temperate regions. The Miocene form *Dicrocerus* is close to the ancestry of the deer. It was about the same size as the living roe deer (*Capreolus*) and had small antlers with long, bony, basal regions. One of the largest fossil deer was the giant deer *Megaceros*, which is very well known from Pleistocene deposits in Ireland where its remains are often recovered from peat bogs. *Megaceros* is closely related to the living red deer (*Cervus*) and had huge spreading antlers with a maximum span of over 4 metres, the largest ever developed.

The bovids are the most successful artiodactyls, and since middle Miocene times they have become the dominant medium-sized herbivores. They are now at the peak of their development and radiation. Bovids are primarily warm-climate, plains-dwelling animals; the key to their success probably lies in their great specialization to this environment and their very efficient digestive system and dentition. The bovids and other higher ruminants (giraffes and deer) have a complex type of stomach consisting of

Sivatherium

four compartments each with a different function. Food is passed to the first stomach compartment after very little chewing; thus a concentrated period of time may be devoted entirely to food collecting. Stomach juices in the first compartment soften and moisten the food and when the animal is at rest it is regurgitated and chewed. After the 'cud' has been chewed it is passed to the other stomach compartments for complete digestion. The ruminant stomach contains populations of small, single-celled animals — protozoa — which are able to digest cellulose. This is important as cellulose forms a large percentage of plant food but mammals are unable to digest it. However, the ruminant can digest the protozoa and is thus able to utilize an otherwise unavailable part of the food. Rabbits and hippopotamuses use protozoan populations in a similar way. The cheek teeth of bovids are very high-crowned as a specialization for grazing, whereas the cheek teeth of deer and giraffes are relatively low-crowned as these animals are mainly browsers. The bovids also have specializations similar to those of horses for plains dwelling; they have long limbs, the feet are functionally two-toed, the brain is large and the sense organs are highly developed.

Dicrocerus

Megaceros

Fossil mammals throughout the world

Palaeolagus

Leptomeryx

Fossil mammals are relatively rare in deposits of Palaeocene and early Eocene age, but several important sites of late Eocene and early Oligocene age are known, including the Fayum in Egypt which has yielded the remains of early elephants, seacows and hyraxes described in the section on plant-eating mammals. Many rich fossil mammal localities are known from North America and Europe, but there are few sites of early Tertiary age in Asia and very few pre-Pleistocene mammalian remains are known from Australia.

Oligocene rocks in the White River region of Dakota and Nebraska, U.S.A., contain one of the richest fossil mammal faunas in the world. They have yielded tens of thousands of specimens representing faunas living in open country, woodland and swamps in early and middle Oligocene times. The animals are unlike those living today, but most of the major groups of living mammals are represented in what was a complete, balanced fauna. Small mammals were well represented and included many insect-eating forms such as early moles, shrews and hedgehogs; another of these small mammals – *Leptictis*, is one of the last surviving members of the group which is ancestral to the modern insectivores, bats, rabbits and rodents. Some of the earliest known rabbits including *Palaeolagus* and many rodents including *Ischyromys* were present, occupying the small herbivore and gnawing niches.

The flesh-eating mammals are particularly interesting in that the fauna represents a transitional stage with both the Creodonta and Carnivora being important. However the creodonts were declining and only hyaenodontids are present, with *Hyaenodon* represented by several species. There are many members of the Carnivora including some of the earliest dogs such as *Daphoenus*; small weasel-like forms; cats such as *Dinictis*; and sabre-toothed cats such as *Hoplophoneus*.

The large and medium-sized herbivores from the White River are also interesting since the artiodactyls and perissodactyls almost equally shared the herbivorous niche, though in numbers of individuals the artiodactyls were dominant. This is the earliest

Orycteropus

Dicerorhinus

Brachypotherium

fauna in which the artiodactyls had gained such importance and represents a transitional stage in the decline of the perissodactyls and the ascendancy of the artiodactyls. Numerous perissodactyls were present in the fauna including the small swamp- and wood-land-dwelling horse *Mesohippus*; the tall fast-running rhinoceros *Hyracodon*, the more typical hornless rhinoceros *Caenopus*; and the huge double-horned *Brontotherium*. The artiodactyls included the giant pig-like entelodont *Archaeotherium*, the anthracothere *Bothriodon* which was amphibious and similar to the hippopotamus in habit; the small hare-like traguloids *Hypertragulus* and *Leptomeryx;* the four-horned *Protoceras*; the gazelle-like camel *Poebrotherium*; the aquatic artiodactyl *Leptauchenia*; the clawed artiodactyl, *Agriochoerus*; and *Merycoidodon*, which was a small herd-living, browsing or grazing ruminant.

Miocene faunas are well known from many parts of the world and contain some modern forms. Faunas from North and East Africa collected in the past forty years have given us a wide knowledge of conditions on that continent in early Miocene times. Small mammals are well known from the East African faunas and include bats, insectivores, rodents, rabbits, monkeys and apes. The earliest known aardvark, *Myorycteropus*, is present and was already very similar to the modern form, *Orycteropus*. Flesh-eating mammals include members of the Creodonta and Carnivora including the largest known creodont. The herbivores were advanced and the initial development of the modern herbivore fauna was evident. Rhinoceroses were common and include *Dicerorhinus*, which is a member of the same genus as the living Sumatran rhinoceros; *Aceratherium*, which was a hornless long-limbed, plains-dwelling form; and the short-limbed heavily-bodied hornless form *Brachypotherium*, which was probably hippopotamus-like in appearance and way of life. Clawed chalicotheres were also present, but horses had not reached Africa and their place was taken by the specialized *Megalohyrax*. The proboscideans included the elephant-like gomphotheres and the bizarre deinotheres with their downturned lower tusks. The artiodactyls included pigs and anthracotheres which were an important part of the total fauna; while tragulids and giraffoids were together the dominant medium-sized herbivores, with the short-necked giraffoid *Prolibytherium* common in North Africa. The first gazelles and antelopes were also present though relatively rare at that time in Africa; however by middle Miocene times they had become common.

Pliocene deposits at Pikermi and Samos in Greece are among the richest fossil mammal-bearing deposits in the world and our knowledge of European Pliocene mammals is very complete. Flesh-eating mammals included *Ictitherium*, which was about the size of a badger but is related to the hyaenas; and true hyaenas (*Hyaena*) which were members of the same genus as the striped hyaena; sabre-toothed cats were also present. The herbivores included the rhinoceroses *Dicerorhinus* and *Diceros*, the latter being in the same genus as the living black rhinoceros. Chalicotheres, gomphotheres and deinotheres were also present. The three-toed horse *Hipparion* was common in Greece and throughout the whole of southern Eurasia from France to China. The browsers included tapirs and the large hyrax *Pliohyrax*, and the grazers included goats, gazelles and antelopes. Large pigs were common and giraffes were numerous with the okapi-like *Palaeotragus* and *Samotherium*, the short-limbed *Helladotherium* and the very long-limbed *Bohlinia*, which is closely related to the modern giraffe. By Pliocene times the faunas of Eurasia, Africa and North America had assumed a modern aspect and included many forms obviously closely related to living mammals.

Hipparion

The mammals described in the rest of this book were part of a fauna which lived in North America, Eurasia and Africa and for most of the Tertiary free migration between these areas was possible. The situation in South America throughout the Tertiary was very different as the continent was almost totally isolated by a seaway until nearly the end of the Pliocene and the fauna developed in almost complete isolation during this period of over 60 million years. However the South American fauna demonstrates that a balanced ecological system can develop even in the absence of

Caenolestes

Thylacosmilus

Prothylacynus

most important mammalian groups and for this reason the South American mammals are described in some detail. In late Cretaceous times a string of islands provided a tenuous link between North and South America and by travelling from island to island over this link some elements of the northern fauna reached South America. Such a mode of dispersal is known as 'island hopping' and tends to be selective. Four major groups – marsupials, edentates, condylarths and notoungulates – reached South America in this fashion in early Tertiary times; and rodents and primates followed in late Eocene or Oligocene times when the island chain was again fairly complete. The South American fauna was thus very unbalanced since multituberculates, creodonts, carnivores, artiodactyls, perissodactyls, insectivores and lagomorphs were not represented and the environments and modes of life usually pursued by members of these groups were thus available for exploitation by members of the colonizing groups.

The marsupials had been important in North America in Cretaceous times but with the exception of Australia they were a relatively insignificant element in the faunas of the rest of the world during the Tertiary. In South America they radiated to become the main insect-eating and flesh-eating mammal and were represented by such forms as the surviving *Caenolestes*; by the extinct *Thylacosmilus* which had long upper canines and was similar to the sabre-toothed cats in appearance and habits; and by *Borhyaena* and *Prothylacynus*, which were the dominant medium-sized flesh-eating animals, and correspond to the cats and dogs in the rest of the world. The marsupial carnivores remained short-limbed and long-bodied and were probably not very successful in open country; moreover no large flesh-eating mammals evolved. The probable reason for this is not paralleled anywhere else in the world. A group of large, flightless birds known as the phororhacoids is thought to have occupied the large flesh-eating niche in South America, thus excluding the mammals from this way of life. *Phororhacos* from the Miocene of Patagonia stood over 2 metres in height, and had long, very strong legs indicating good

Theosodon

Thoatherium

Macrauchenia

running ability, and a huge skull with a strong, very deep, curved beak.

The plant-eating mammals of South America were a very mixed group. The xenarthran edentates (anteaters, sloths and armadillos) were even more bizarre and far more important than surviving forms suggest. The giant ground sloths were probably browsers, but roots probably also featured in their diet. *Megatherium* was one of the largest forms, having a body about the size of an elephant and huge claws. The form of its pelvis suggests that it was to some extent bipedal and the fore-limbs were either used to pull down vegetation or to dig. *Megatherium* survived until historic times and successfully invaded North America, as did the huge plains-living, grazing armadillo *Glyptodon* which had a massive bony carapace. Some glyptodonts developed large, heavily armoured tails which were probably used for defence. Smaller armadillos were also important throughout the Tertiary and the Miocene form *Peltephilus* developed a pair of small horns on its nose.

Five mammalian orders originated from the Condylarthra in South America. Of these the Litopterna was the most successful; it included plains-dwelling herbivores such as *Theosodon* and the horse-like *Thoatherium* which was a plains-dwelling grazer with a single toe on each foot in which the reduction of the splint bones was more advanced than in the modern horse. *Macrauchenia* was a large camel-like herbivore with a long neck and short trunk; it was probably a browser and may have been giraffe-like in habit. Two other orders, the Astrapotheria and Pyrotheria, were relatively important, and included members which were hippopotamus- or rhinoceros-like and presumably inhabited the banks of rivers. *Astrapotherium* was a large, heavily-built animal with large front teeth and high-crowned cheek teeth; it ranged from the Oligocene to the late Miocene. *Pyrotherium* was about the size of a hippopotamus and it also had large front teeth though its cheek teeth with their transverse crests were similar to those of *Deinotherium*. The notoungulates were the most important South American herbivores. This group originated in Asia or North America and entered South America during the Palaeocene. Rabbit-like notoungulates such as

Megatherium

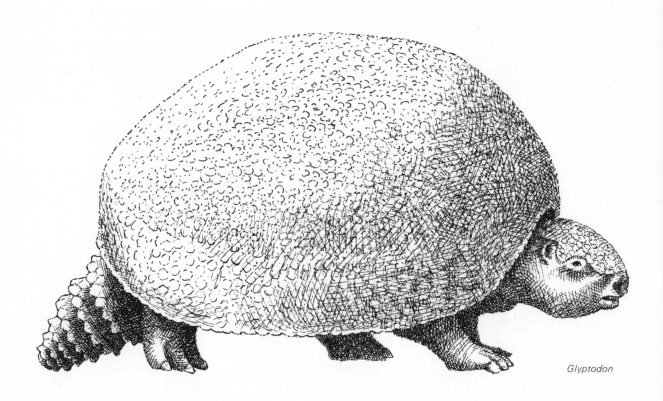

Glyptodon

Pyrotherium   Protypotherium

Astrapotherium

Interatherium

Toxodon

the hegetotheres and interatheres *Interatherium* and *Protypotherium* developed, as well as large rhinoceros-like forms such as *Toxodon* and *Nesodon.*

Rodents entered South America towards the end of the Eocene and gave rise to the Caviomorpha, which is still the characteristic group of South American rodents and includes the living American porcupine, *Erethizon*, the chinchilla, guinea-pig, coypu and capybara. South American rodents are generally larger than those of the rest of the world and during the Pliocene forms such as *Protohydrochoerus* and *Telicomys* developed, being about the size of a tapir and a small rhinoceros respectively. The rodents obviously occupied the small gnawing and herbivore niches and were also able to become medium-sized herbivores, a way of life from which they have been excluded in the rest of the world by the artiodactyls and perissodactyls.

Many of the herbivore groups became extinct in South America before the end of the Pliocene, when the establishment of the Central American land bridge permitted North American mammals to invade South America in large numbers. Groups such as the marsupial carnivores, which had direct counterparts in North America, rapidly became extinct and many northern groups became established in the south. Some forms, such as the opossum, *Megatherium* and *Glyptodon*, had no exact equivalents in the north and these forms were able to invade North America successfully. Although forms such as the armadillos and anteaters survived in South America, in general the South American mammals became extinct in the face of competition from their more efficient northern counterparts.

Fossil mammals in Britain

Coryphodon

Palaeotherium

Fossil mammals are relatively poorly represented in British deposits. Early Eocene localities in the London area have yielded a fairly extensive mammalian fauna which agrees closely with North American faunas of the same age, indicating that free migration was possible at that time between North America and Eurasia, and implying the existence of a land connection, probably across the northern Atlantic area. Fossil plants in the same deposits indicate climatic conditions similar to those of the Malayan region today, with dense tropical forest and high rainfall. The fossil mammals include several species of *Hyracotherium*; the large herbivore *Coryphodon*; the early primate *Platychoerops*; and the marsupial *Peratherium*, which is the only marsupial to occur outside Australia and the Americas and is also present in European Eocene, Oligocene and Miocene deposits.

Late Eocene and early Oligocene mammals are well known from southern Hampshire and the Isle of Wight. At that time the area was an estuary with dense forests consisting of palms, water plants and many tropical forms of vegetation. The mammals include small forms such as the marsupial *Peratherium*, insectivores, primates and rodents. The flesh-eating mammals were creodonts such as *Hyaenodon*, and members of the Carnivora such as the wolverine-like miacid, *Viverravus*. The main herbivores were the small, primitive artiodactyls *Dacrytherium*, *Cebochoerus* and *Choeropotamus*; and larger forms such as the anthracothere *Bothriodon*, which was very common. Perissodactyls were represented by the rhinoceros *Ronzotherium*; and also by the two palaeotheres, *Palaeotherium* and *Plagiolophus*, representing an early radiation from the ancestral stock of the horses which produced forms that were the European counterparts of the tapirs and true horses of North America. *Palaeotherium* was about the size of a tapir and was probably similar in habits while *Plagiolophus* had longer legs and feet and was probably a plains-living animal.

Fossil mammals are unknown from the Miocene of Britain and Pliocene mammals are poorly represented but include gomphotheres and the seacow *Felsinotherium*. The British Pleistocene fauna was very rich and is well known from hundreds of fossil localities. The fauna included elephant, mammoth, rhinoceros, tapir, hippopotamus, bison, giant deer, sabre-toothed cat, lion, hyaena, bear, wolf, panda, wolverine, horse and reindeer.

Fossil mammals are relatively rare in Britain and are unlikely to be encountered by the amateur collector, however their remains have been discovered and can still be found on the Isle of Wight, at Barton and Hordle in Hampshire, at several places in the London area and in East Anglia.

Index